CONTENTS

Who's That Baby?

Parents: Stu and Didi Pickles.

Bestest Friend: Chuckie Finster.

Favouritest food: Reptar Bars - they turn your tongue green!

Favouritest toy: Star ball.

Greatest skills: Opening the playpen with a toy screwdriver, having adventures.

Scariest moment: Being sent through the mail system.

View on the world: A great big amusement park.

Most likely to say: "A baby's gotta do what a baby's gotta do."

Name: Tommy Pickles.

AKA: Tommykins (by his mom).

Age: One year.

Hair: Not much.

UP UP AND AWAY

WHEN AN ADVERTISEMENT FOR BALLOON RIDES WAS POSTED THROUGH HIS DOOR, TOMMY COULD HARDLY BELIEVE HIS EYES...

LOOK AT THIS PICTURE, CHUCKIE! PEOPLE BEING FLOATED THROUGH THE SKY IN A BALLOON!

WOW! IMAGINE BEING EVEN HIGHER THAN YOUR DAD'S SHOULDERS! THAT'S SCARY!

IT'D BE GREAT! HEY, CHUCKIE. I GOTTA IDEA! WE COULD BE FLOATED, TOO!

UH-OH.

I'VE STILL GOT SOME BALLOONS FROM SUSIE'S PARTY. WE JUST TIE THEM TO MY WAGON AND THE WORLD'S OUR LOBSTER!

I'M NOT SURE I WANT TO BE FLOATED, TOMMY. I LIKE IT RIGHT HERE!

BESIDES, WHAT IF WE GET FLOATED TOO HIGH? WHAT IF WE GET STUCK ON MARS? WHAT IF THEY DON'T HAVE COOKIES ON MARS?

DON'T BE SUCH A FRAIDY CAT, CHUCKIE. I'LL DRIVE AND I'LL MAKE SURE WE DON'T GO TOO HIGH. COME ON, LET'S GET THE BALLOONS.

I'M TELLING YOU, TOMMY, THIS IS NOT A GOOD IDEA!

HERE WE ARE! NOW ALL WE NEED IS OUR BASKET!

YOU KNOW, REPTAR'S ON TV SOON. WE COULD JUST GO WATCH THAT!

BUT TOMMY IS DETERMINED TO SEE THE WORLD...

THIS IS GOING TO BE REAL GOOD FUN, CHUCKIE! WHERE SHALL WE GO FIRST?

UM, YOU KNOW, I THINK THERE'S ONLY ROOM FOR ONE BABY IN THERE, TOMMY!

SOON...

WE'RE READY FOR TAKE OFF, CHUCKIE! ONCE ALL THESE TOYS ARE OUT, WE'LL BE UP, UP AND AWAY!

ULP!

WHEN ANGELICA POPPED TOMMY AND CHUCKIE'S BALLOONS TO STOP THEM BEATING HER HOME, SHE BROUGHT THEM ALL DOWN TO EARTH WITH A BUMP...

BACK IN THE REAL WORLD...

WHAT HAPPENED? AM I ALL RIGHT?

ANGELICA CHEATED, THAT'S WHAT HAPPENED!

YOU DUMB BABIES WERE THE CHEATS! I WAS WINNING AND YOU...YOU...

...WE GOT PAST YOU SQUARE AND FAIR, ANGELICA! YOUR BASKET WAS JUST TOO HEAVY TO BEAT US!

ANGELICA, I SAW YOU BURST THE BABIES' BALLOONS FROM THE WINDOW! THAT'S NOT NICE, IS IT? AND YOU PUSHED THEM OVER!

NOW YOU'RE TALKING GARBAGE, I –

HELLO, AUNT DIDI. I WAS JUST PLAYING WITH THE BABIES AND –

ANGELICA PICKLES!

ULP!

AND SO...

HEY, THESE ARE GREAT BALLOONS! WE COULD GO ROUND THE WORLD AGAIN SOON, CHUCKIE!

YES, AUNT DIDI.

HUMPH!

YOU CAN SHOW HOW SORRY YOU ARE BY GIVING THE BABIES YOUR BALLOONS TO REPLACE THE ONES YOU POPPED. THERE'S A GOOD GIRL.

8

Where In The World?

There are lots of places Tommy and Chuckie didn't visit on their balloon adventure. Unjumble the letters on the luggage below to find some of the places they hope to see next time! The answers are at the bottom of the page.

DINAI

SUSIRA

AMACIAJ

NIPAS

TRINABI

NAAPJ

9

The Cookie Run

7

6 You find some stale toast on the floor. Miss a go to eat it.

5

8

9

10 Yikes! Who spilt that juice? Slip forward 2 squares.

SPIKE

16 Get on your trike! Speed on 3 squares.

1.

17

18 Stu spots you and carries you out of the kitchen. Go back to start.

19

20

Didi has left a full jar of cookies on the kitchen table - just within the Rugrats' reach. And guess what? They're chocolate ones! Yummy!

Here's your chance to have some fun at being a Rugrat! All you need to play this game is a dice. To make the counters, ask a grown-up to help you cut them out when you've read your annual -

they'll last longer if you paste them to some card. Up to six people can play. Each player chooses a counter and places it at the start. You need a six to get into the kitchen, then you just take turns to work your way round to the table. The first one to reach the cookies is the winner!

KITCHEN

3

2

1

Spike's in the way and he's just asleep! Miss a go while you climb over him.

12

13

14

21

22

KOOKIES

11

Who's That Baby?

Favouritest toy: Teddy bear.

Greatest skills: Being a scaredy cat, worrying.

Scariest moment: Getting his head stuck in a sock.

View on the world: One big scare after another.

Most likely to say: "You guys, I don't think this is such a good idea."

Name: Charles Finster Jr.

AKA: Chuckie.

Age: Two years.

Hair: Out of control.

Parent: Charles Finster Sr. (Chas).

Bestest Friend: Tommy Pickles.

Favouritest food: Reptar cookies.

The Race Is On

BANG! BANG! THUD! THUD! BANG!

Didi smiled to herself as she passed the basement door and heard her husband working hard in his workshop below. Stu was a toymaker who loved to design elaborate new toys for little Tommy and kitchen gadgets for Didi. He would work on an invention for days at a time, then proudly burst from his workshop with his completed product. Didi knew that he had already spent quite some time on his latest contraption and was due to show it off at any moment.

"Well, he's sure working up an appetite down there," she chuckled to herself. "I'd better go and fix some lunch."

While Didi was in the kitchen, she heard Stu run up and down his stairs several times, bringing bits and pieces up from the basement. He chatted excitedly to Tommy and Chuckie as he assembled his new toy.

"This is destined for big things, kids," she heard him say. "This is the toy that's going to put Pickles Industries on the map!"

Didi smiled again as she wondered how

many times she had heard that phrase. She gathered up all the lunch things on a tray and went into the living room.

"Hello, dear. Lunch is rea - ooops!"

Didi tripped over something and sent the lunch tray flying.

"Careful, Deed!" Stu called from the hallway. "That's my latest prototype you just stepped on!"

Didi kneeled up to find that she had

tripped over some sort of track that Stu had set up. She then turned to find herself looking up the nostrils of a large toy horse on wheels.

"Oh, this looks interesting, Stu," she said, peering at the animal and picking lunch up from the floor. Stu came in the room with another horse and set it down next to the first. He put his hands on his hips and sighed a satisfied sigh as he looked round the room at the track and horse jumps that were all his own work.

"What you see here, Deed, is a life-sized horse-racing game," he explained. "I'll show you how it works!"

Pulling on his old stetson for added effect, Stu placed one of the horses on the track and got on it. Jiggling up and down and shouting "Giddy up, girl!", he started to trundle round the track. Didi decided she was going to have to spoil her husband's fun.

"That's a fabulous game, dear," she declared, "but it's far too big to have indoors. You'll have to take it outside."

Stu stopped jiggling and slid off his horse. He turned to the babies in the playpen.

"Show's over, boys," he said with a shrug of the shoulders. "Looks like we're being sent into the garden."

Stu was soon setting his new game up again outside. Tommy and Chuckie were having great fun trotting round the garden as if they were horses, and they were soon joined by the twins, Phil and Lil. It wasn't long before Angelica, too, came to see what was going on.

"Pah! Only dumb babies pretend to be horses," she scoffed, as she watched the others galloping round. "Let's have a proper race!"

Chuckie was quite happy to carry on trotting as before, but Tommy could never resist a challenge.

"Okay, Angelica," he said. "What's the deal?"

"Like I said, a proper race on the horses. I win, you bring me a jar full of cookies..."

"Where are we going to get a jar full of cookies from?" interrupted Chuckie.

"Your problem, not mine, Chuckie," Angelica smirked.

"Well, we might win, Angelica!" insisted

Tommy. "So what do we get?"

"I just happen to have..." Angelica pulled a green foil packet from her pinafore, "...a pack of Reptar bars. Winner takes all, huh?"

Chuckie hesitated, but Tommy was ready to go. The race was on!

Angelica and the babies all got on their horses. As they waited for the race to start, Chuckie's imagination started to run away with him as he suddenly found himself on a real horse at a race course, in a real horse race...and they were off! His long, ginger hair shook and his glasses danced around on his nose as his horse galloped along with the others. He imagined Phil and Lil being thrown from their horse at the first fence...then Tommy was thrown into a pond by his. Now it was up to him to race for the Reptar Bars against Angelica! Faster and faster his horse galloped, so fast that he had to cling to its mane so as not to fall off. Too fast! The horse was going too fast! He was beating Angelica, but he was starting to panic. He yelled and yelled that he wanted to get off, but...

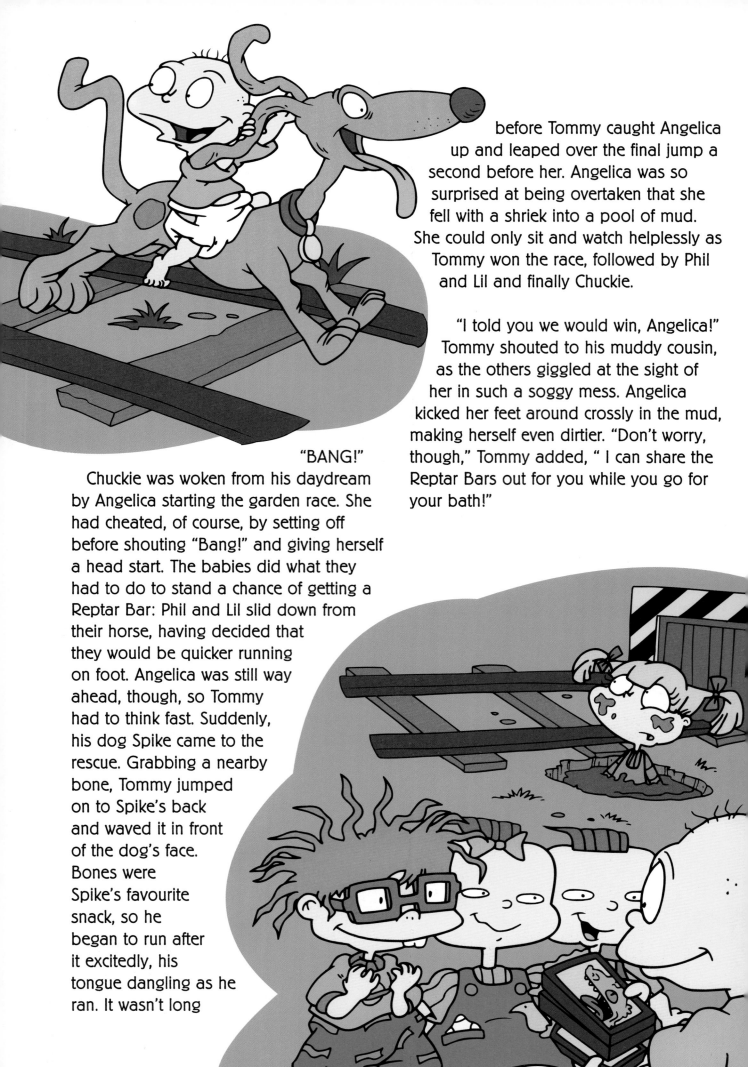

before Tommy caught Angelica up and leaped over the final jump a second before her. Angelica was so surprised at being overtaken that she fell with a shriek into a pool of mud. She could only sit and watch helplessly as Tommy won the race, followed by Phil and Lil and finally Chuckie.

"I told you we would win, Angelica!" Tommy shouted to his muddy cousin, as the others giggled at the sight of her in such a soggy mess. Angelica kicked her feet around crossly in the mud, making herself even dirtier. "Don't worry, though," Tommy added, " I can share the Reptar Bars out for you while you go for your bath!"

"BANG!"

Chuckie was woken from his daydream by Angelica starting the garden race. She had cheated, of course, by setting off before shouting "Bang!" and giving herself a head start. The babies did what they had to do to stand a chance of getting a Reptar Bar: Phil and Lil slid down from their horse, having decided that they would be quicker running on foot. Angelica was still way ahead, though, so Tommy had to think fast. Suddenly, his dog Spike came to the rescue. Grabbing a nearby bone, Tommy jumped on to Spike's back and waved it in front of the dog's face. Bones were Spike's favourite snack, so he began to run after it excitedly, his tongue dangling as he ran. It wasn't long

Round And Round The Garden

The Rugrats are having another race round the garden on their trusty steeds. Who's going to win this time? Follow the paths to see who will reach the winning post!

17

Boys Keep Out!

Angelica and Susie are really good friends...sometimes! Use your favourite pens or crayons to colour in this picture of them playing together.

Twin Trauma

THE DEVILLE TWINS, PHIL AND LIL, WOULD OFTEN FIGHT. ONE FINE AFTERNOON, THEY WERE PLAYING IN THEIR GARDEN WITH THE OTHER RUGRATS...

OKAY, CHUCKIE, YOUR HOUSE IS ON FIRE AND I'M COMING TO RESCUE YOU!

IT IS? YOU ARE?

NO ONE SAW LIL WANDERING OFF...

I'M GOING TO FIND A MAGIC GARDEN!

THIS IS MAGIC WATER. I'M GONNA MAKE THIS FLOWER BIGGER THAN A HOUSE!

WOW!

LIL WENT INTO HER OWN LITTLE WORLD...

MEANWHILE...

OKAY, SO WHO LOST THE DRIVER FROM THE FIRE TRUCK? LIL, YOU HAD IT LAST! LIL!

SHE'S GONE, PHIL. MAYBE SHE GOT SAD AFTER YOU YELLED AT HER.

LIL! LI-I-I-L! WHERE ARE YOU?

15 MINUTES LATER...

OH, MY! SHE'S BEEN GONE HOURS NOW! LIL! LILLIAN!

LIL! DON'T BE SAD! COME BACK!

LIL! HELLO-O-O!

OH, NO! THIS IS 'COS I SAID I WISHED LIL WOULD GO AWAY FOREVER! NOW SHE'S GONE, AND IT'S ALL MY FAULT!

LIL HAS DISAPPEARED AFTER AN ARGUMENT WITH HER TWIN BROTHER. WITHOUT HIS OTHER HALF, PHIL IS LIKE A BEAKER WITHOUT JUICE...

BACK IN THE GARDEN...

WELL, WE LOOKED EVERYWHERE NOW.

YEAH. MAYBE SHE FOUND A WAY TO MAKE HERSELF INVISTIBLE OR SOMETHING.

YEAH, RIGHT. (SIGH!)

WAIT TILL PHIL SEES WHAT I GOT! MAGIC BUGS AND STUFF!

HI, GUYS! WHY DO YOU ALL LOOK SO SAD?

HEY, PHIL! I'VE BEEN TO A MAGIC GARDEN AND I GROWED SOME GIANT FLOWERS AND GUESS WHAT I GOT FOR YOU?

GIANT BUGS! WELL, THEY WERE GIANT WHEN I CAUGHT THEM. THEY SHRINKED A LITTLE ON THE WAY BACK.

LIL! IT'S SO GREAT TO SEE YOU!

IT IS?

I ONLY WENT TO THE MAGIC GARDEN, PHILLIP! WHAT'S WITH THE SOPPY STUFF?

I MISSED YOU! AND I'M GLAD YOU'RE MY SISTER! IN FACT, YOU'RE THE BESTEST SISTER IN THE WHOLE WIDE WORLD EVER!

?

HOORAY!

Bags of Bugs

Tommy and Chuckie have been collecting creepy crawlie pets...but some of them have escaped! They did have three caterpillars, three flies, three ants, three butterflies, three centipedes, three spiders and three ladybirds. Count the creepy crawlies below to see which four have escaped.

Answer: A caterpillar, a butterfly, a spider and a ladybird have gone off to frighten Angelica!

23

The Rugrats on...FOOD!

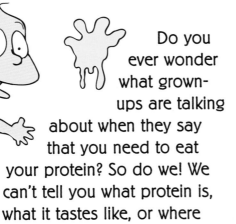

Do you ever wonder what grown-ups are talking about when they say that you need to eat your protein? So do we! We can't tell you what protein is, what it tastes like, or where you can buy it, but here are some of our thoughts on food and stuff!

Yeeeuck!

A Word from Phil and Lil on Eating Out

The best food you can find is in the garden. Anything that's small and moving is good - worms and bugs are our favourites. If you can't find anything slimy or crunchy, earth is pretty tasty. If it's raining and you have to eat indoors, the yummiest titbits are those mouldy old pieces of forgotten food that you can find under the sofa - mmmmm! If the grown-ups have been hoovering there, though, there's always something interesting in the dog's bowl.

A Word from Chuckie on Greens

My Dad's cool. He's always telling me to eat my greens. Greens are delicious. You can get all sorts of different kinds. The ones I've tried are Reptar bars, Reptar cookies and best of all, Reptar cereal - they're lean, they're mean, they turn your milk green! Greens are what I like to eat most of all. My most unfavourite food that I don't like is vegebles.

10 Things To Do With Your Food Except Eat It

1. Cover the mat under the high chair with it - that's what it's there for!
2. Play with it.
3. Wash your hair with it.
4. Mash it into tiny pieces (then it looks as if you've eaten some).
5. Hide it behind the video.
6. Use it as a face cream.
7. Feed it to your favourite teddy.
8. Drop it in your juice.
9. Plaster your bib and clothes with it.
10. Feed it to your parents - whether they like it or not!

A Word from Angelica on Eating Up (or Not)

Take it from me, you need to watch those growd-ups when they give you your food. Anything that looks interesting is a trap, so beware. Orange dinosaur shapes, for example, are chicken dressed up as Reptar, and anything that looks like a happy face is bound to have vegebles in it. To make mealtimes worthwhile, take your time eating all the boring stuff - then you'll find that the nearest growd-up will offer you cookies if you eat it up. Throw it to the dog when they're not looking, then enjoy your cookies!

A Word from Tommy on Dressing for Dinner

I like to spill a whole beaker of juice down myself just before dinner, so that I get to wear a fresh, clean outfit to spill food on. My Mom always gives me a bib with a nice picture on it to wear over my chest, but I'm not sure why - most of my food seems to go on my arms and legs. Dishes make good hats, especially when they're still full of food. The best part of dinner is a splash in the bath afterwards!

A Word from Spike on Dogs' Dinners

Woof!

Birdy Blues

It was the summer vacation and Susie and her family were going away for the weekend. They had been looking after the nursery school parrot for the holidays and although Susie had nagged to take the bird with them, her dad, Randy, had put his foot down and persuaded Drew to parrot sit.

"Look who's come to stay with us, Angelica," Drew smiled when the bird arrived. He placed the cage on a table and squatted down to take a look. "His name's Rainbow. He's a parrot. Do you see the bright colour of his feathers?"

Angelica squatted down beside her dad, who was making clicking noises with his tongue in an attempt to communicate with the parrot.

"Who's a pretty boy, then?" he said to it. Angelica looked at him and frowned.

"He's not as pretty as me, is he,

Daddy?" she pouted.

"Of course not, cupcake. You're the prettiest girl in the world, you know that! Now, if we talk nicely to Rainbow here, he might just talk back to us. Would you like that?"

"Yeah! Make the bird talk, Daddy! Make him say 'Angelica's pretty'!"

Drew stuck a finger into the parrot's cage and waggled it.

"What's your name? What's your name?" he asked, trying to mimic a parrot. "Come on, boy, tell us your - OW! YEEEARGH!"

Drew snatched back his finger. The parrot hadn't taken too kindly to being pestered and had given him a sharp peck.

"He bit me!" Drew spluttered, nursing his invisible injury. Angelica smiled: maybe her dad would pay some attention to her now.

"Can I bandage your finger, Daddy?" she asked.

"In a moment, sweetie." Drew marched off and quickly returned with a large cloth that he used to cover the cage.

"Dumb parrot!" he muttered. "I was only trying to be friendly."

The next day, Angelica was playing in the living room when she was startled by a voice.

"My name's Rainbow! My name's Rainbow!"

It was coming from the birdcage! She ran over to it and pulled off the cover. Rainbow fixed her with his beady eyes and squawked again.

"Good girl! Good girl!"

"Wow!" exclaimed Angelica. "You're not as dumb as I thought!"

Rainbow flapped his wings, making Angelica jump back. As he settled down, one of his brightly coloured feathers floated to the floor. She picked it up and

tickled her hand with it, then used it to tickle Rainbow under the chin.

"Hmm. Maybe we could have some fun," she murmured thoughtfully. "Hey, Rainbow. How 'bout coming out of that smelly old cage for a while? Yeah, I think that's a great idea, too!"

Hearing her father's approaching footsteps, Angelica threw the cover back on the cage and ran over to the sofa, deftly picking up a book as she went.

"You all right, honey?" Drew asked. He was ready to go out to the garden with a tray full of plants. "I just have to take these out. I won't be long."

"Okay, Daddy!" sang his daughter,

looking up from her book and smiling sweetly.

"And don't touch that bird cage!" he called back as he left the room. "He might give you a peck, too!"

As soon as Drew had gone outside, Angelica ran to fetch a coat hanger from her room.

"You see, birdy, I'm not touching the cage," she sniggered as she wiggled the hook in the cage door to open it, "the hanger is!"

"Good girl! Good girl!" shrieked Rainbow excitedly.

Angelica cackled as the parrot flew out of his cage as soon as the door opened.

"Come here, birdy!" she called, and the parrot landed on her finger. "Now fly away again!" she ordered, and Rainbow did just that. She giggled even more and danced with glee.

"This is too good! Wait till I show the others!"

Angelica had soon sneaked off to Tommy's house to show off her new pet. With the parrot perched on her arm, she strolled proudly into the garden and coughed to get Tommy and Chuckie's attention.

"Meet Rainbow, babies!" she said. "He's a very clever parrot and he does everything I say!"

Tommy and Chuckie stopped playing and stared in awe at the coloured bird.

"Can he talk?" Tommy asked.

"A course he can!" replied his cousin.

"Can he fly?"

"A course he can!"

"C-can he bite?" Chuckie asked nervously.

Angelica crouched down so the parrot was close to Chuckie's face.

"Only if I tell him to, Chuckie!" she answered,

menacingly. Chuckie was afraid.

"WAAAAAAAAAH!" he yelled, startling the parrot. Angelica gasped as Rainbow squawked and flew off her shoulder.

"Wow! I didn't hear you tell the birdy to fly away, Angelica!" said Tommy.

"You dumb babies!" Angelica exclaimed, clapping her hands to her cheeks in panic. "Look what you made me do! Rainbow's scaped and it's all your fault!" She watched helplessly as the parrot settled high in a tree.

"Rainbow!" she called. "Rainbow! Nice parrot, come down now! Come on! Here, birdy, birdy!" Quickly losing her patience, she stamped her foot. "Oh, for Bob's sake, will you just come down! Dumb bird!"

"I don't think he wants to come down," Tommy observed.

"I can see that!" snapped Angelica. She sat down sulkily. "What am I gonna do? He's Susie's parrot. She'll be so mad if I lose him."

Tommy put a hand on his cousin's shoulder.

"Don't worry, Angelica. We'll catch the birdy," he assured her. He picked up his

29

little fishing net and held it up. "We can get him with this!"

"Yeah, right. Quick!" Angelica suddenly shrieked and jumped up. Rainbow had flown from his branch and swooped down towards them. She leaped at him, arms outstretched, and Tommy waved his net around, but neither of them managed to catch him. Chuckie, alarmed by the flapping of wings and general commotion, scurried under a wheelbarrow to hide.

"There he is! Go!" The two cousins threw themselves at the fence where the bird had landed, but ended up catching each other. By the time they'd scrambled to their feet, Rainbow had flown into the street and sent a cyclist careering into the kerb.

"After him!" ordered Angelica. She and the babies gave chase, following the parrot's path of destruction through the streets. First, it sped past a window cleaner and sent him and his bucket of water toppling off his ladder. Round the corner, it swooped down past a dog on a lead, which then went into a barking frenzy

and ran circles round its owner until both landed in a tangled heap on the pavement. The bird finally came back to where it had started from and landed on the roof of Angelica's house.

"Oh, no!" she whined. "Look where it's landed now! We'll never get him down from there!"

"What're you gonna do?" asked Tommy.

Angelica did the only thing that was left for her to do:

"DA-A-A-A-D-D-D-D-Y-Y-Y-Y!"

Drew was soon at Angelica's side, calming his sobbing daughter with one arm and scratching his head with the other as he looked up at the parrot on the roof.

"They did it, Daddy!" Angelica wailed, pointing at the bewildered babies. "They let Rainbow out of his cage! I tried to stop them, really I did, but they just went right ahead and - and -"

"It's okay, cupcake," said Drew. "Don't cry. Daddy will, um, get the birdy down."

He fetched a ladder and climbed gingerly up it. As he went up on tiptoe on the top rung and stretched his arm out towards the parrot, a sweat broke out on his forehead.

"N-nearly there..." he muttered. "Come on, p-pretty parrot!"

At last, he caught the bird and wobbled down the ladder with it.

"Hooray! You're so smart, Daddy!" beamed Angelica, relieved that she wouldn't be in trouble with Susie.

She danced behind him as she followed him into the house. As he went to shut the cage door, he saw the hanger.

"Angelica! This is one of your hangers, isn't it?" he said sternly. "Did you let Rainbow out of his cage? Tell the truth, now."

Angelica put a finger to her mouth. "Um..."

"No ums!" Drew snapped. "That's a very naughty thing to do! You're not having any candy for a whole week!"

The following morning, the doorbell rang. It was Susie, coming to collect Rainbow.

"Hello, Susie!" Drew greeted her as he opened the door. "Did you have a good time?"

"Yes, we had a lovely time, thanks," she replied. "Was Rainbow okay?"

"Oh, he was just fine," Drew smiled wanly. "In fact, it was a real pleasure looking after him, wasn't it, Angelica?"

"Just great," Angelica replied glumly. She was suffering from sugar withdrawal already. "Just great."

31

Catch That Parrot!

When Susie's parrot escaped from Angelica's house, she thought she would never catch him again! All these parrots look similar, but only one is the real Rainbow from the story. Which one is he?

1

2

3

4

5

6

7

8

32

Who's That Girl?

Favouritest food: Cookies, chocolate, Reptar Bars and ice cream - all at once!

Favouritest toy: Her doll, Cynthia.

Greatest skills: Singing, dancing, throwing tantrums, showing off.

Scariest moment: Getting covered in baby germs.

View on the world: A big jar of cookies - and they're all for her!

Most likely to say: "The babies did it!"

Name: Angelica Pickles.

AKA: Cupcake (by her dad).

Age: Three years.

Hair: Beautiful.

Parents: Drew and Charlotte Pickles.

Bestest Friend: Her daddy.

33

The Tummy Monster

...IT'S A MIRACLE THAT HE'S GROWING AT ALL! YOU GOT ANY IDEAS, DIDI?

WELL, CHARLES, LIPSCHITZ RECOMMENDS THAT YOU MAKE FOOD AS ATTRACTIVE AS POSSIBLE. HAVE YOU TRIED REPTAR-SHAPED FISH CAKES WITH BROCCOLI VOLCANOES?

MEANWHILE, THE RUGRATS WERE PLAYING QUIETLY NEARBY. ALL OF A SUDDEN...

GRRROOOWWWWL!

WHAT WAS THAT FUNNY NOISE?

IT SOUNDE LIKE A BIG TIG THE JUNGL

THERE IT IS AGAIN!

IT'S COMING FROM CHUCKIE'S TUMMY!

GRRROOOWWWWL!

YOU KNOW WHAT THAT MEANS, DON'T YOU, CHUCKIE?

IT MEANS ONE OF THOSE MONSTERS THAT CRAWLS UP YOUR NOSE AND GOES TO LIVE IN YOUR TUMMY HAS CRAWLED UP YOUR NOSE AND GONE TO LIVE IN YOUR TUMMY! HA!

YOU MEAN...

...THERE'S SOMETHING ALIVE... WRIGGLING AROUND...IN MY TUMMY?

WAAAAAAAAAAAAAA

DON'T WORRY, CHUCKIE! WE'LL MAKE SURE YOU DON'T FALL ASLEEP!

IF YOU'RE HAPPY AND YOU KNOW IT CLAP YOUR HANDS...!

UM, HI, BABIES! I SAID, HI, BABIES! WHAT'S ALL THE NOISE FOR?

HI, SUSIE! DO YOU WANT TO HELP US KEEP CHUCKIE AWAKE? HIS TUMMY WAS GROWLING AND ANGELIC TOLD US IT WAS A MONST THAT CRAWLED UP HIS NOSE WHILE HE WAS ASLEEP AND...

BOOM! BOOM!

YEAH, CHUCKIE! WE'LL KEEP THOSE MONSTERS AWAY!

WAIT, WAIT A MINUTE! ANGELICA TOLD YOU IT WAS A MONSTER?

YEAH, WHY? DO YOU THINK IT MIGHT BE SOMETHING...ULP!...EVEN WORSER?

CHUCKIE, I THINK YOUR TUMMY'S JUST A LITTLE HUNGRY. OUR TUMMIES SOMETIMES MAKE GROWLING NOISES TO LET US KNOW WHEN WE SHOULD EAT. WAIT THERE.

UM, SOME REPTAR CEREAL, A PIECE OF FISHFINGER, TWO PEAS, SOME GRASS, A BUG...I THINK THAT'S IT.

NO, CHUCKIE. I DON'T THINK THERE'S A MONSTER AT ALL. WHAT DID YOU EAT TODAY?

PEAS? YUCK!

YEAH. THEY WERE AN ACCIDENT. THEY WERE STUCK TO THE FISHFINGER.

MRS. PICKLES, PLEASE MAY I HAVE SOME TOAST TO GIVE TO CHUCKIE? I THINK HE'S HUNGRY.

(MUNCH! MUNCH!) SUSIE, YOU SURE THERE'S NO TUMMY MONSTER?

I'M SURE, CHUCKIE. I THINK MAYBE I SHOULD HAVE A LITTLE WORD WITH ANGELICA...

OF COURSE, DEAR.

HEH! MAYBE YOU SHOULD COME AND LIVE WITH US FOR A FEW DAYS, SUSIE! CHUCKIE DOESN'T SEEM TO EAT ANYTHING I GIVE HIM.

Barby Babies

The Rugrats and their families are all having lots of fun at the Pickles' barbecue party. Look closely at the picture, then see if you can solve the puzzles.

Stu has been a little careless and dropped some hot dogs on his way to the barbecue grill! See if you can spot the 10 sausages that he's dropped.

Some of Tommy's cuddly toys have found their way into the garden. How many can you find altogether?

Unjumble the letters on the balloons to find out what day the party is on.

Those twins are at it again! Join the dots to discover what Phil and Lil are fighting over.

You'll find the answers at the bottom of the page.

Who's That Baby?

Names: Phil and Lil DeVille.

AKA: The twins.

Age: 15 months.

Hair: More than Tommy - just.

Parents: Betty and Howard DeVille.

Bestest Friends: Each other.

Favouritest food: Anything that's been on the floor.

Favouritest toys: Whatever the other one's playing with.

Greatest skills: Getting dirty, getting each other into trouble.

Scariest moment: Being apart for more than five minutes.

View on the world: One big, full dinner plate.

Most likely to say: "Eat it first, ask questions later."

Hic-Hic-Hiccups!

Hic! Hic! Hic!

"Okay, kids, you play nice, now. I'll just be right here."

Stu was babysitting the Rugrats. Having made sure there were plenty of toys in the babies' playpen, he settled down in his favourite armchair with a bowl of popcorn in front of the television. Hardly a minute had passed before he was startled by a scream from the kitchen. Thinking something terrible had happened, he jumped up and rushed out, scattering popcorn on the carpet.

"What is it, honey?" he asked Angelica when he found her in the kitchen.

"L-look, Uncle Stu," she stammered. "It's a tranchler!"

Stu peered behind the cookie jar that Angelica had been raiding.

"It's just a little spider, Angelica."

"But it's scary!" she whined.

"Okay, okay. Let's put him outside, shall we?"

While Stu was making the kitchen a spider-free zone, Tommy had reached through the playpen bars to grab some of the stray popcorn. He popped it in his mouth, sucked it for a second, then swallowed.

"Mmm!" he said, and reached for some more. After several mouthfuls, he guzzled some milk.

"Wow!" he exclaimed to the others. "I don't know what my dad was eating, but it sure was - HIC!" Everyone looked at Tommy, astonished.

"It sure was what?" asked Phil.

"HIC!"
hiccupped Tommy

again. "Hey, guys! HIC! Something keeps coming out - HIC! - of my mouth! HIC!"

"Is it slimy?" grimaced Lil as she tried to look more closely.

"HIC! HIC!" Tommy's hiccups were getting louder!

"Th-there's something down there!" said Chuckie.

"Yeah! It barked at us!" agreed Lil.

"Did you eat a puppy, Tommy?" asked Phil.

"No, just this stuff my dad was - HIC!" Tommy put more popcorn in his mouth, but hiccupped it right back out again. The babies were alarmed.

"Yaaaah!" yelled Chuckie as he was showered with popcorn.

"Tommy's getting ready to pop!" warned Phil.

"Run!" Lil shrieked, as they all took cover at the other end of the playpen.

"What's going on?" Angelica had recovered from her spider trauma and had come in to see what the commotion was.

"We're trying not to get Tommy all over us when he pops!" explained Lil. Angelica looked at Tommy.

"HIC!"

"You dumb babies!" she jeered. "He's not gonna blow! He just has the hip-ups - and they can last for years and years!"

"I don't want to - HIC! - have the hip-ups forever!" Tommy objected.

"Well, only a big scary scare can stop em, Tommy," declared Angelica. "You just go about your baby day, an' when you least expect it, I'll cure you!"

"Thanks, Angelica...HIC!" Tommy smiled.

Angelica disappeared with the twins to think up some scary tricks.

"I need something to - HIC! - scare me now, Chuckie," Tommy said, turning to his friend. "I'm gonna - HIC! - look for some s...HIC! - some s...HIC!"

"Soup? Stickers? Sunflowers?" Chuckie suggested.

"Scary stuff! HIC!"

Chuckie sighed as he followed Tommy into the kitchen. Most stuff was scary to him.

"A monster - HIC! - lives in here," Tommy explained as he went over to the waste disposal unit. "I hear him growl when he - HIC! - eats our leftodors!"

"Oh, no!" Chuckie backed away as Tommy went to open the door. "Not the monster, Tommy! If he eats your leftodors, he must be really - AAAAAARGH!" he screamed as Angelica jumped out wearing a scary mask. Tommy barely flinched.

"Hi!" he smiled. "Didja think of a good way to scare me yet? HIC!"

"Aw, Tommy's not scared of anything!"

said Phil.

"Humph!" Angelica took off the mask and flounced out of the kitchen. "Let's see how brave you are when you meet the bogeyman!" she called back.

Later, as Tommy was looking for the bogeyman himself, he and Chuckie were pushed into a dark cupboard by Phil and Lil. Before either of them could say anything, they heard a groaning beside them: "Whoooooooooh!"

"It's the boogerman!" cried Chuckie.

"It's 'bogeyman', dumb baby!" interrupted the bogeyman from the darkness. "Now, help me find my head. It's got mushy brains hanging out - and squishy eyeballs!"

The two babies felt someone grab their wrists and put their hands on something soft and stringy and squidgy.

"AAAAARGH! I feel 'em!" yelled Chuckie.

"HIC!" added Tommy.

Light suddenly flooded the cupboard as curiosity got the better of the twins and they opened the door. Chuckie was delighted to see that his hand wasn't stuck in brains and eyeballs, but spaghetti and meatballs.

"It's pisghetti!" he grinned and licked his fingers. Tommy looked at it glumly.

"You were supposed to scare me - HIC! - not feed me," he said.

Angelica decided that enough was enough. She was going to skip the soft stuff and go straight to the worst thing ever: her scare machine. She went into the garage and built a tower of the most

frightening things she could find: some Halloween masks, a rubber bat, a ghostly white sheet draped over a broom, a pumpkin lantern, a jack-in-the-box and even a real spider! She went to find Tommy and quietly left a bottle of milk on a skateboard tied to a piece of string near him. Having run back to her scare machine, she pulled on the string to lure Tommy into the garage. Tommy came in and was about to pick up the milk, when CRASH! BANG! BOING! THUD! Angelica's scare machine collapsed on top of her! Tommy ran over to his cousin, followed by the other babies.

"Are you all right, Angelica?" he asked, worried.

"Leave me alone!" snapped Angelica.

"Hey, Tommy! Your hip-ups have stopped!" noted Chuckie. Tommy paused, then grinned.

"Yeah! They have!" he exclaimed. "I was scared that Angelica was hurt! It cured me!"

The babies all looked over at Angelica, sitting on the floor in her heap of scary stuff. They gasped as a strange noise came from her mouth:

"HIC!"

What's Up, Tommy?

Fill the words in the grid below to find out what's wrong with Tommy!

45

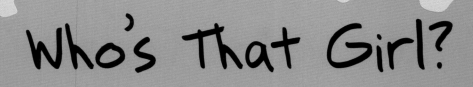

Who's That Girl?

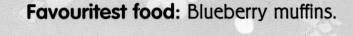

Favouritest food: Blueberry muffins.

Favouritest toy: Her bike.

Greatest skill: Sharing, solving the babies' problems.

Scariest moment: Losing her toys when moving house.

View on the world: A place that needs her help.

Most likely to say: "My sandbox is your sandbox."

Name: Susie Carmichael.

AKA: The baby (by her parents).

Age: Three years.

Hair: Lots of plaits.

Parents: Lucy and Randy Carmichael.

Bestest Friend: Angelica Pickles...sometimes.

Lost Treasure

WHEN DIDI CAME BACK FROM SHOPPING WITH LOTS OF NEW CLOTHES, TOMMY, CHUCKIE AND ANGELICA HAD A GREAT TIME...

SHEESH! SHOPPING FOR NEW CLOTHES IS SOOOO TIRING, STU!

I DON'T KNOW HOW YOU MANAGED TO BECOME SO GOOD AT IT, DEED!

LATER, IN DIDI'S BEDROOM...

LET'S PLAY A DRESSING-UP GAME, BABIES.

I DON'T THINK WE SHOULD DO THAT, ANGELICA!

WHAT D'YA THINK, CHUCKIE?

YOU LOOK REAL FUNNY, TOMMY!

WHAT ELSE IS HERE?

I'M A FAMOUS STAR!

YOU'RE NOT AS FAMOUS AS ME, CHUCKIE!

LOOK AT THESE, BABIES! PROPER BIG SHOES! JUST MY COLOUR, TOO.

GUESS WHO I AM, BABIES?

I'M A KING, SO YOU CAN'T BE ME, ANGELICA!

AND I'M A-A PRINCE, SO YOU CAN'T BE ME, EITHER!

WEARING DIDI'S HIGH-HEELED SHOES WASN'T EASY...

I'M A- A...OOOOOH!

OH, BE QUIET, YOU DUMB BABY!

I KNOW! ARE YOU PRETENDING TO BE A CLOWN, ANGELICA?

AS DIDI REACHED FOR THE BEDROOM DOOR HANDLE...

TOMMY? CHUCKIE? ARE YOU IN THERE?

HIDE, CHUCKIE!

YOU SAY TOMMY AND CHUCKIE MADE ALL THIS MESS, ANGELICA?

UH-HUH! COME OUT, BABIES!

!!!

I GUESS IT'S TIME I WENT HOME NOW, AUNTIE DIDI! BYE, BYE!

AUNTIE DIDI WON'T MISS THIS FOR A WHILE!

LATER...

HMMMM!

I TELL YOU, I'VE LOOKED EVERYWHERE FOR THE NECKLACE I BOUGHT TODAY, BETTY!

THAT'S STRANGE, DEED! MY FAVOURITE RING AND A BRACELET HAVE DISAPPEARED, TOO!

Tasty Treasure

Tommy, Chuckie, Phil and Lil are racing to the best treasure of all: Reptar cookies! Show them how to get to the monster feast before their tummies start to rumble.

The Orangefish

Chuckie's dad, Chas, was looking after Tommy for the afternoon and had decided to take the two babies to the fair.

"Okay. First stop the hoop-la stall!" he smiled. "I'm going to win you a prize, Chuckie!"

As Chas threw hoops, Tommy and Chuckie looked at the toys on the stall.

"Just look at that big teddy bear, Tommy!" Chuckie whispered, spotting the star prize.

"Wow! He's almost as big as Reptar!" exclaimed Tommy.

"Hooray!" Chas suddenly yelled. "I did it, Chuckie! I won you a prize! Hey, excuse me! My prize, please! I won!"

The babies looked at each other excitedly.

"Okay, Chuckie. Close your eyes and hold out your hands."

As Chas strolled in front, Chuckie looked with disappointment at the little fish in its water-filled bag.

"It's not even gold! It's orange!" he complained.

"Never mind, Chuckie!" Tommy said brightly. "It coulda been worse. Your dad coulda wonned you a bug or something! Anyways, I think he's kinda cute."

"You do?" Chuckie raised his eyebrows. "Well, yeah...I s'pose he is!"

"And I bet this is the smartest fish in the world, Chuckie!"

"Yeah, and he's gonna be my second bestest friend - after you, Tommy!"

Chuckie did as he was told until he felt something in his palms. He opened his eyes.

"It's a goldfish!" grinned Chas. "I know how you kids love to have pets! Watch out, coconut shy, here I come!"

On the way home, Chas stopped off at a pet shop to buy things for his son's new pet. From the moment Chuckie got his 'orangefish' home, the two became inseparable. Chuckie would put the fishbowl in his brick trolley and take his new friend with him everywhere: to the garden, to Tommy's house, to the park. With his new friend, Chuckie was less of a fraidy cat. Tommy was very surprised one day to see Chuckie go down the playground slide without hesitating, clutching his little fish bowl.

"I'm not scared of anything when orangefish is with me!" he explained.

Chuckie would even take his pet with him at bathtime and place the bowl on a chair near the tub.

"Look, orangefish!" he would shout as he splashed around in the bubbles. "I got a bowl to swim in, too!"

One afternoon, Chuckie decided to let his orangefish out of the bowl for some air. As Tommy watched, Chuckie plunged a ladle into the fish bowl and tried to

catch his pet.

"I can't get him, Tommy," he complained. "He keeps slippering out!"

"Here, let me try," offered Tommy. He rattled the huge spoon round the bowl for a second or two, then flicked it up, sending the fish somersaulting through the air.

"There you go, fishy!" he smiled.

"Yeah!" added Chuckie. "Time for a breather!"

The babies watched as the fish flailed on the floor.

"See, I told you he was smart!" said Chuckie. "He's doing sit-ups like they do on the TV!"

"Wow!" gasped Tommy.

"NO! CHUCKIE!" The babies were startled by Chas' raised voice. He had spotted the fish on the floor and came rushing over.

"WAAAAAAH!" bawled Chuckie.

"I'm sorry, Chuckie," Chas said,

scooping up the fish and plopping him back in his bowl. "I didn't mean to make you jump. It's just that you mustn't take the fishy out. He needs his water to stay alive!"

Chuckie stopped crying and gazed into the

54

sea's way too big for my orangefish, Tommy. He might get lost!"

Tommy thought for a moment.

"Hey, Chuckie! I gotta idea!" he exclaimed. "We could put him in the pond in the park. Then he could swim lots and you could still see him sometimes!"

Chuckie didn't really want to let his orangefish go, but he agreed that it was for the best. They took him on their trip to the park that afternoon and stood by the pond. Chuckie looked down into the bowl and knelt at the water's edge.

"You're moving to a biggerer home, orangefish," he sniffled, then tipped his pet into the water. "Bye. I'm gonna miss you. You're the bestest second bestest friend I ever had."

"Orangefish is gonna be just fine, Chuckie," Tommy insisted. "Just look at all the friends he has!"

Chuckie held the empty bowl up to his face and looked through the glass. His fishy friend was gone. He would never forget him...at least not until he'd had an ice cream.

bowl again.

"He can't swim very far, can he, Tommy?" Chuckie observed. "Maybe we should get a bigger bowl for him."

"You know, I sawed a programme about fishies, Chuckie," Tommy replied. "They live in a big place called the sea. Look," he ran to fetch one of Chuckie's books. He opened the page to show an undersea scene with lots of different coloured fish swimming around. "You see, Chuckie? That's orangefish's real home. Even your dad couldn't buy a bowl that big. Maybe you should send him back there."

"But that

Who's That Dog?

Favouritest food: Dog food, bones and slippers.

Favouritest toy: Anything that squeaks.

Greatest skills: Digging holes, chasing his tail until dizzy.

Scariest moment: Swallowing a Christmas tree decoration.

View on the world: A huge garden full of interesting smells.

Most likely to say: "Woof!"

Name: Spike

AKA: That dumb mutt (by Angelica).

Age: Older than Tommy.

Hair: Short and usually muddy.

Family: Didi, Stu and Tommy Pickles.

Bestest Friend: Tommy Pickles.

56

Chuckie's Bad Hair Day

60

Socks Box

Angelica is sorting through her socks - she always seems to be losing them! How many pairs and how many odd socks does she have?

Load Of Garbage!

The Rugrats can have fun anywhere, even amongst the rubbish bins! These two pictures look the same, but there are lots of differences between them - see how many you can spot.